CONTENTS

The ecology of the Great Lakes states and North and South Dakota includes three major biomes (**MB** 648). These are the grasslands of North and South Dakota and parts of Illinois, the coniferous forests of northern Minnesota, Wisconsin, and Michigan, and the deciduous forests of Indiana, Ohio, and part of Illinois (**MB** Fig. 52–8). The presence of the Great Lakes adds to the ecological diversity by altering the amount of precipitation and the temperatures in surrounding regions.

When the pioneer farmers first entered what is now the eastern border of North and South Dakota, they found tall-grass prairies that stretched for hundreds of miles. Rainfall was (and still is) relatively abundant, and in those early days grasses such as big bluestem, switch grass, and Indian grass were dominant and sometimes grew over eight feet tall. The grasses had for centuries prevented erosion of the soil, which was rich and deep, ideal for farming. Today these tall-grass prairies are farms producing crops such as wheat, corn, and soybeans, while much of the land is covered by roads and houses.

Farther west, as rainfall decreases, the prairies become predominantly mixed, with both short and long grasses. In the dry country even farther west, short grasses, such as little grama grass and buffalo grass, grow only a foot or so high. Original prairie with bison and prairie dogs can still be seen in parks such as Badlands National Monument of South Dakota and Theodore Roosevelt National Memorial Park of North Dakota.

In western Minnesota there is a rapid transition from grassland to coniferous forest. In the northern region of the Great Lakes states, the coniferous biome extends south from Canada and is reflected in the vegetation and animal life of Minnesota, Wisconsin and Michigan.

In the most northern regions of Superior National Forest of Minnesota, spruce and fir are well adapted to the bitter cold winters, cool summers, and short, wet growing seasons. Small stands of deciduous trees, such as aspen and yellow birch, are scattered throughout this lake country. Spruce-fir forests are found also in Nicolet National Forest in Wisconsin and in the northern Michigan peninsula.

Farther south, white, red, and jack pine become the dominant evergreens. Even more prevalent are the aspen-birch transitional forests that reflect logging activity. Most of the spruce-fir-pine forests in regions such as the boundary-waters canoe area of Minnesota are largely secondary growth. Many of the animals and birds have survived the heavy logging. Moose and bear still roam freely, although wolves are rarely seen.

Still farther south, the pine forest blends into a mixed forest of pine, maple, beech, birch, and various poplars. This transitional forest supports the pulp industry in Wisconsin and Michigan and, like many mixed forests, harbors a wide variety of animal and bird life, such as white-tailed deer and ruffed grouse.

The mixed forest blends into the deciduous-forest biome characteristic of Ohio, Indiana, and parts of Illinois. Cold winters and warm summers, a longer growing season, rich soil, and fairly even rainfall support the various forest types that make up this biome. The oak-hickory forest is a principal climax-forest type. Other forest types include the elm-ash-cottonwood forest bordering the Mississippi, the maple-basswood forest in northeastern Illinois, the beech-maple and oak-cypress forests in Indiana, and the white pine-hemlock and buckeye-maple forests in Ohio.

In addition to moderating temperatures and increasing precipitation, the Great Lakes shorelines harbor many diverse communities. Some, such as the Indiana sand dunes and Sleeping Bear Dunes of Michigan, are unique. The Indiana dunes provide a classic example of an orderly ecological succession from sandy beach to beech-maple climax forest.

WILDFLOWERS

Goldenrod (*Solidago spp.*) of various species bloom all summer. Well over 70 species occupy many different habitats in this region (**MB** 671). Adaptive radiation offers some explanation for this phenomenon (**MB** 172). Some species have adapted to swamps or flood plains, while others prefer open fields or stony city lots (**MB** 18).

Goldenrod has a long, flexible stem that ends in a plumelike cluster of tiny golden flowers. These flowers are primarily insect-pollinated. The wind-pollinated ragweed is the villain that causes hayfever. In the fall goldenrod galls can be collected and studied.

Common Burdock (*Arctium minus*) is an imported species that has spread rapidly. In disturbed fields and city lots its broad leaves give it a decided advantage in competing with other plants in the struggle to survive (**MB** 167). The plant is a biennial. Its fruits are produced in the second year. The seeds are dispersed in fruits, or burs, that stick to the fur of passing animals or to clothes (**MB** 340). A magnifying glass can be used to see how the stickers are designed to hold. The seeds inside the burs are classed as achenes (**MB** 338, Table 27–1).

Common Strawberry (*Fragaria virginiana*) is a low-lying, inconspicuous plant found in well-drained soils in fields and along hedgerows. The leaves are pinnately veined, hairy, and toothed. Vegetative reproduction is accomplished by runners (**MB** Fig. 27–2). The flowers are small and white with five rounded petals, and quickly give rise to strawberries, which are examples of accessory fruits. The seeds embedded in the red fleshy fruit are achenes (**MB** 339, Table 27–1). Wild strawberries appear in early June and are delicious eating.

Field Bindweed (*Convolvulus arvensis* L.), or wild morning glory, lacks strong supportive tissue (**MB** 285). It grows horizontally along the ground and gains height by twisting around stable objects such as other plants. Wild morning glories are positively thigmotropic (**MB** 325). They are typically seen along roadside fences and can be found growing in empty city lots and in backyards throughout the suburbs. They are very tolerant of exhaust fumes, soot, and other pollutants (**MB** 710). Their white or pink trumpet-shaped flowers attract insects, which serve as pollination agents (**MB** 332). The fruits are capsules (**MB** 338, Table 27–1).

Evening Primrose (*Oenothera biennis* L.) is a biennial (**MB** 285). The first year a germinating seed gives rise to a flat rosette of leaves. These rosettes can usually be found close to second-year plants that bear a central, erect stalk a meter or more in length that carries the flowers. The ovaries develop into capsules which split along their sides to release their seeds (**MB** Fig. 27–13). The life cycle is then repeated. You can actually watch the flowers of this plant open in the twilight (**MB** 325). Moths are attracted by the bright yellow color and serve in pollination (**MB** 400).

Bloodroot (*Sanguinaria canadensis* L.) (**MB** 281, Table 22–1) gets its name from a bright red sap that oozes from cut stems or roots. In early spring young buds on thick rhizomes grow upward (**MB** Fig. 24–16). Flower buds pushing through the soil are protected by leaves wrapped around them. As they surface, the leaves unfold and the flowers open. The deeply lobed leaves and the snow-white flowers are beautiful, though the flowers last only a day or two before going to seed. The leaves function to store food in the rhizomes for next year's flower buds. New plants emerge each spring from seed and rhizome. Indians used the bloodroot to paint their bodies.

White Trillium (*Trillium grandiflorum*) helps to cover the barren spring ground of the northern forests of Michigan, Wisconsin, Minnesota, and northern Illinois (**MB** 649). Its flower parts are all in threes or multiples of three, indicating that the plant is a monocot (**MB** 281). It has three large green leaves, three sepals, and three large white petals. It has six stamens and three stigmas that unite into a style (**MB** Fig. 27-5). White trilliums bloom for only a short time, then turn pink with age. They are soon replaced by more shade-tolerant species (**MB** 680).

Queen Anne's Lace (*Daucus carota*) is an imported species from Europe and a good example of an expanding population (**MB** Ch. 51). A bulldozed lot may quickly be colonized by a sea of the white, disc-shaped clusters of tiny flowers. The function of the small, central purple flowers on some clusters is not known, but their gene frequency may be increasing (**MB** 171). The Latin name *Daucus carota* indicates that the common name "wild carrot" is accurate (**MB** 176). Queen Anne's lace has a large tap root that smells and tastes like a cultivated carrot (**MB** Fig. 24-7).

Dog's-Tooth Violet, or **White Trout Lily,** (*Erythronium albidum*) is first seen in the spring when tiny spear-shaped red leaves poke through the decaying oak leaves on the forest floor. The parallel venation of the leaves shows the dog's-tooth violet to be a monocot (**MB** 281). The leaves trap the sun's energy, and nutrients are transported to corms deep in the forest soil (**MB** Fig. 24-16). The white flowers quickly produce fruit. Vegetative reproduction occurs when shoots grow from the base of the corms to reach toward the surface (**MB** 327). The dog's-tooth violet belongs to the family *Liliaceae (***MB** 281, Table 22-1).

5

Columbine (*Aquilegia canadensis*) is protected by law in some states (**MB** 703). Its flowers are usually bright red with a yellow center. The unusual shape, the long curved stems, and the deeply lobed leaves make the columbine one of our most beautiful wildflowers. It is an herbaceous perennial with a hardy root system that survives the winter to send up new shoots each spring (**MB** 286). Columbines grow in rocky, wooded, well-drained areas. Their red color attracts hummingbirds, which visit them for nectar (**MB** 333). When picked, they wilt rapidly (**MB** Fig. 25-8). They are difficult to transplant.

Dandelion (*Taraxacum officinale* Weber) is highly competitive with grass. Its deep taproot (**MB** Fig. 24-2), spreading horizontal leaves, and reproductive capacity are all factors working for its survival (**MB** 167). Humans pay millions of dollars for herbicides to destroy it, only to watch it return next year. Meanwhile, the quality of the groundwater worsens (**MB** 705-710). Dandelions belong to the family *Compositae*. Their single heads contain many individual flowers. The seeds that develop are achenes (**MB** 338, Table 21-1). The progression from flower to fruit can be studied, since both are often available at the same time (**MB** Fig. 27-9).

Nodding Wild Onion (*Allium cernum*) is one of several species of wild onion that grow in this region. Wild onions may be recognized by large numbers of relatively thick, long leaves that first appear in the spring. If there is doubt about them, their odor is unmistakable. Once established, the young plants immediately start to store food in underground modified stems, or bulbs (**MB** Fig. 24-16). The bulbs survive the winter and give rise to new plants in the spring. The flowers of the nodding wild onion are pink and hang in clusters from a curved stem. They appear in July and August and rapidly form fruit.

Black-Eyed Susan (*Rudbeckia hirta*),

is a roadside beauty that doesn't seem to mind the fumes of passing cars (**MB** 710). It is prominent in fields and prairies where clusters of these flowers are noticeably oriented towards the sun (**MB** Fig. 26-7). Their bright orange-yellow color attracts bees, butterflies, and other insects, the agents of pollination (**MB** Fig. 32-4). The black disc, or "eye," of the black-eyed Susan is a mass of small, complete flowers. Yellow pollen can sometimes be seen covering their anthers (**MB** Fig. 27-5). Rows of sterile flowers encircle the complete, centrally located flowers. The seeds serve as foods for many different birds as well as mice and other animals.

White Sweet Clover (*Melilotus alba*)

has been beneficial, unlike most plants not indigenous to this area. It grows well on disturbed, even compacted ground, offering cover and protection against erosion (**MB** Fig. 52-3). Like other species of the pea family (*Leguminosae*) its deeply penetrating roots show the nodules that function in nitrogen fixation (**MB** Figs. 48-4, 48-5). Flowers of the white and yellow sweet clover are arranged along a central stalk. Their sweet odor attracts insects which feed on nectar. The pea-shaped flowers are structured to accommodate visiting bees. Honey made from clover is prized (**MB** 403-6).

Milkweed (*Asclepias spp.*) is usually

about one meter high. Its thick stem, broad, paired leaves, and terminal cluster of green-purple flowers make it stand out along road sides and in open fields and woods. Bees that leave its flowers can be observed to have tiny sacs of pollen attached to their legs (**MB** 332). The bitter, milky sap that oozes from cut veins discourages most grazing animals and insects, with the exception of the black and red milkweed beetle and the larvae of the monarch butterfly (**MB** 676). A large pod that develops from one of the flowers contains many seeds which are dispersed by the wind (**MB** Fig. 27-13).

Fragrant Water-Lily (*Nymphaea odorata*) is important in pond and lake ecology and succession (**MB** Figs. 49-2, 50-8). Ducks, muskrats, and beaver feed on various parts; moose consume them in great quantities. Water-lilies reflect both water and land environment. Stomata on the upper surface of their floating leaves allow for gas exchange (**MB** Fig. 23-3). Oxygen gas produced by photosynthesis fills the spaces in stems and leaves and is used in respiration (**MB** 292, Fig. 23-4, Table 23-2). After pollination by insects, fruit develops and floats free from the parent plant (**MB** 340).

Grasses are among the most important flowering plants. They serve as a basic food source and prevent soil erosion (**MB** Fig. 24-2, 48-12). The prairie grasses, like buffalo grass and big bluestem, were once dominant plants in the grasslands of North and South Dakota (**MB** 651). The stolons of buffalo grass and the rhizomes of big bluestem helped insure their survival (**MB** Fig. 24-16). These and other prairie grasses are now largely replaced by cultivated grasses such as wheat, corn, and lawn grass. The flowers of grasses are small and imperfect, but their stamens and pistils are recognizable when magnified (**MB** Fig. 27-5). Some widespread wild species like crab grass are highly competitive (**MB** 167), horizontal stems sending down adventitious roots (**MB** 302) at their nodes and replacing cultivated grasses.

Poison Ivy (*Rhus radicans*) can be a creeping ground plant, a thick-stemmed vine, or a shrub. It has palmately compound leaves (**MB** Fig. 23-8) of three leaflets on a long stem. Sometimes the leaflets appear shiny with an oily film, and sometimes they have a reddish tinge. This oily substance causes a severe skin rash in some people. If the poison ivy is a climbing vine, the stems have aerial rootlets (**MB** 302). Tendrils are lacking (**MB** 296). The flowers are small and yellow. The fruits are small white berries on which birds such as the flicker and pheasant feed.

Eastern Cottonwood (*Populus deltoides*), is a fast-growing tree that can reach a height of 30 meters (100 feet). It often stands out as a lone tree that marks the site of a pond, stream, or low wet areas on farm land. The fluttering motion of the leaves in a breeze makes cottonwoods easily recognizable from a long distance. This fluttering, twisting motion is due to the flattened petioles, a characteristic of all poplars (**MB** 294). The leaves are large and triangular with coarse teeth. On a breezy, sunny, summer day the transpiration rate for a cottonwood can be very high (**MB** 314).

The sexes are separate in cottonwoods, with staminate and pistillate catkins on separate trees. After the pollen is blown from the anthers, the male catkins drop to the ground. Later the female trees release large numbers of seeds, each attached to a tuft of "cotton," a parachute that carries the seed on the wind (**MB** 340).

Eastern Cottonwood
White Oak

White Oak (*Quercus alba*) is the state tree of Illinois. The leaves are alternate and simple and show a pinnate venation (**MB** Fig. 23–8). They are deeply lobed with smooth margins and a pale green undersurface. The oak takes about 50 years to reach maturity but then produces acorns in massive numbers each year. An oak's reproductive life is long; some white oaks are over 500 years old.

The acorns of the white oak mature in one year, while those of the northern red oak, which may be in the same forest, take two years to mature. Most of the acorns produced serve as food for other organisms. Very few grow into mature trees.

The bark of the white oak is light in color. Oak bark is rich in tannin (**MB** 699), which is used in tanning leather. The wood of the white oak (**MB** 304–305) is dense, heavy, strong, and beautiful, good for floors, furniture, paneling, and for ships.

American Elm

American Elm (*Ulmus americana*) can be recognized from a long distance by its acute branching and rounded crown. Elms have long graced the streets of towns and cities. Their upper branches may intermingle to form a domelike canopy (**MB 654**).

The leaves are simple, with short petioles and double teeth. The flowers are perfect and appear in spring before the leaves emerge (**MB 330**). The wood of the elm is tough and hard to split, and is used extensively for furniture.

Once plentiful, this beautiful shade tree is being rapidly depleted by Dutch elm disease (**MB** 240, 244). This fungal disease first appeared in Ohio in 1930. It is spread by the European elm bark beetle. Viral diseases are also taking their toll of elms (**MB** 191). Scientists are trying to save the American elm from the fate of the American chestnut, which is on the verge of extinction because of fungal disease (**MB** 244).

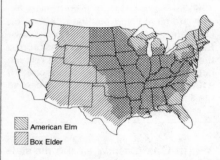

American Elm
Box Elder

Box Elder or Ash-Leaved Maple

Box Elder or **Ash-Leaved Maple** (*Acer negundo* L.) has, like many organisms, an *L* after the species name to indicate that this tree was first classified by Carolus Linnaeus (**MB 176**). The box elder is planted in some regions as a shade tree. Although it is fast-growing, it is also short-lived. It is a hardy tree that can grow in semi-arid regions and city lots, but it flourishes along stream banks. The leaves are pinnately compound, usually with three but sometimes five to seven leaflets (**MB** Fig. 23–8). The leaflets on a single leaf are often of different shapes, some lobed like maple leaves, others ovate like ash leaves. Box elders have either pistillate or staminate flowers. The female produces the typical double samaras of maples (**MB** 338, Table 27–1). The blades of the samara twirl the fruit away from the parent tree (**MB** 340). The red and black box-elder bug is often found on these trees. The wood of the box elder is lightweight and soft. It is used as pulp and sometimes for interior finishing.

Bur Oak (*Quercus macrocarpa*), like all oaks, is firmly anchored in the earth by a large taproot (**MB** 299) and thick, horizontal roots that may extend even beyond the reach of the overlying branches. The branches are thick and heavy, and the smaller ones seem to grow in all directions. Although the branching is crooked and gnarled, the overall shape of a tree growing alone is a rounded dome (**MB** Fig. 24–9). The bur oak is found in a variety of habitats, including well-drained hillsides or moist bottomland, and is a prominent member of the oak-hickory forest (**MB** 651).

The sweet acorns (**MB** Fig. 27–1) of the bur oak provide food for many different animals. These include ruffed grouse, jays, grackles, deer, mice, raccoons, foxes, and chipmunks. A failure in an acorn crop can mean starvation for some animals.

The cup of the bur-oak acorn is fringed with hairlike strands. The bur-oak leaves are deeply lobed, with a bulbous end and with a smooth margin (without teeth).

◨ Bur Oak
◨ Eastern White Pine

Eastern White Pine (*Pinus strobus,* **MB** 179, Table 14–1) is an important member of the northern coniferous and mixed forests (**MB** Fig. 48–10). Like other evergreens, it is a gymnosperm, an ancient type of plant that reproduces by naked seeds rather than with the fleshy fruits of flowering plants (**MB** 280). Young eastern white pines show the effects of apical dominance in their conical shape (**MB** Fig. 24–9). The flexible branches are ideal for shedding snow, as are the needle-like leaves for conserving water, which is a scarce commodity in winter. The eastern white pine is identified by its soft, pliable needles about 8 to 10 cm (3–4 inches) long that are in bundles of five. Their small, female cones contain the naked, winged seeds that are distributed by the wind (**MB** Fig. 22–2). The northern forests of virgin white pine have all but fallen to the axe (**MB** 699). Their white, strong wood, almost free of knots, was and still is used in construction, cabinet making, and interior finishing.

11

Sugar Maple

Sugar Maple (*Acer saccarum*) is a prominent species in the deciduous northern forests (**MB** Fig. 48–11) and the climax species in some areas (**MB** 680). Sugar maples may become large trees. Their leaves have five major lobes and prominent teeth (**MB** Fig. 23–8). Their flowers appear with the new spring leaves. The fruits are double samaras (**MB** 338, Table 27–1).

Sugar maples are often planted as shade trees. They are especially beautiful in the fall when their leaves turn red, orange, and yellow (**MB** Fig. 23–7) before dropping to the forest floor (**MB** Fig. 23–9). Short cold spells in early fall cause even brighter leaf colors. With spring, great quantities of sweet sap, used to make maple sugar, flow up and down the phloem (**MB** Fig. 22–12, Fig. 24–11). Maple wood is used in flooring, furniture, and paneling.

The sugar maple can be distinguished from the Norway maple (**MB** Fig. 23–1) by squeezing the tip of a leaf's petiole. The sap in the Norway will be milky; the sap in the sugar maple, clear.

Sugar Maple
Horse Chestnut Introduced Species

Horse Chestnut

Horse Chestnut (*Aesculus hippocastanum*) is a relative of the Ohio buckeye, the state tree of Ohio. An import from Europe, the horse chestnut has been planted as a shade tree in many states. Some now grow wild in deciduous (**MB** 650) and mixed forests.

The horse chestnut is broad and well-rounded in shape with showy, white, pyramid-shaped flower clusters. The leaves are opposite and palmately compound, usually with seven leaflets (**MB** Fig. 23–8). The petiole enlarges where it attaches to the stem (**MB** Fig. 23–9). The fruits look like green, spiked golf balls. Inside the thick cover is a shiny brown seed with a gray eye. The seeds are seldom if ever eaten by any mammal.

The horse chestnut makes an excellent winter twig study (**MB** Fig. 24–14). Its prominent leaf and bundle scars are clearly seen, and the large terminal bud is easily dissected (**MB** Fig. 24–15).

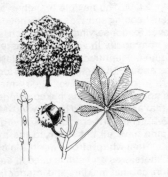

Eastern Red Cedars (*Juniperus virginiana* L.) are conifers (**MB** 279) that are ordinarily treelike and grow to a height of 10 meters (33 feet) or more. However, when the topmost apical buds are continually trimmed, apical dominance (**MB** 322) is altered, and horizontal growth of lateral branches creates the shrublike forms that typically decorate suburban landscapes.

The older leaves of the red cedar, as in most junipers (**MB** Fig. 22–1), are small and scalelike and are pressed against the stem. The new-growth leaves are more needlelike and resemble the leaves of the common juniper (*J. communis*). The tiny, round cones are fleshy and berrylike with a blue, waxy skin. The fruits are eaten by cedar waxwings, warblers, robins, and other birds. The dense branches serve as nesting sites. People use the wood to line cedar chests, where it protects stored woolens against moth larvae (**MB** 407). Unfortunately, the red cedar serves as a secondary host for apple rust fungus (**MB** 248).

▨ Eastern Red Cedars
▧ Frosted Hawthorn

Hawthorns (*Crataegus spp.*) are small shrubs or trees that are often among the pioneer plants that invade open fields in the process of plant succession (**MB** 678). They also make up a large part of the understory in many decidous forests. Most hawthorns are easily recognized by their long, strong sharp thorns which are modified stems (**MB** 308). Their small leaves (about 2 or 3 cm wide) are alternate and toothed, and vary greatly in shape, even on the same tree. Individual species are difficult to identify because of hybridization (**MB** 154) and the large number of varieties. Hawthorns belong to the family *Rosaceae.* Clusters of white, roselike flowers, each with five petals, appear in spring that attract insects such as bees (**MB** 333). The hawthorn's fruits—small applelike drupes (**MB** 338, Table 27–1), serve as food for cedar waxwings, deer, raccoons and other animals, which distribute the seeds (**MB** 340). The seeds of some species lie dormant for two years before germinating (**MB** 343).

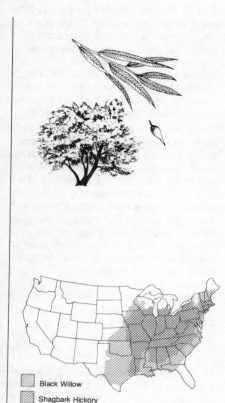

Willows (*Salix spp.*) consist of both trees and shrubs. Their leaves are characteristically long, slender, and pointed. Willows thrive along the banks of streams and ponds. The roots do not penetrate deeply like a taproot but spread horizontally (**MB** 299). Broken willow twigs that come to lie on muddy banks sprout adventitious roots and stems along their length (**MB** 302). Willows are often planted along stream banks to prevent erosion (**MB** 693).

The staminate and the pistillate flowers occur as catkins on separate plants. The furlike structures that give the pussy willow its name are actually staminate flowers. Pollination is by both wind and insects. Bees visit the flowers for pollen and nectar (**MB** 332). Hairlike structures aid in seed dispersal by wind (**MB** 340).

The most popular ornamental willow tree is the weeping willow (*S. babylonica*). The black willow (*S. nigra*) is the only willow commonly used commercially for lumber.

Black Willow

Shagbark Hickory

Shagbark Hickory (*Carya ovata*) gets its name from the ragged plates of bark that peel and curl away from the trunk (**MB** Fig. 24–11). The leaves are alternately compound, usually with five, but sometimes three or seven, large leaflets. The shagbark hickory is one species associated with the climax oak-hickory forest (**MB** 651). Young shagbarks have a rather smooth bark and may appear similar to certain ashes. Ashes, however, have oppositely compound leaves.

Small staminate and pistillate flowers are borne on the same tree in spring. The flowers give rise to tough-shelled nuts, each covered by a green, thick husk that splits along four seams. The nuts of the shagbark are sweet and tasty. They are eaten not only by people but also by mice, chipmunks, and squirrels.

The wood of hickories is hard and strong and can withstand shock without splitting. This makes it ideal for handles for tools and for baseball bats. Pioneers used hickory wood in producing axe handles, plows, wagon wheels and hickory-smoked hams.

Staghorn Sumacs

Staghorn Sumacs (*Rhus typhina*) are shrubby trees that reproduce by seed. Sumacs usually grow in clusters and are pioneer trees in sunny, open areas. They grow rapidly, are short-lived, and are replaced by more permanent shade trees (**MB** 680). In spring the newly formed branches, as well as the leaf stems, are covered with fine hairs. In fall the pinnately compound leaves turn bright scarlet (**MB** 296). Bunches of crimson, fuzzy drupes decorate the ends of the branches (**MB** 338, Table 27–1), which, when they are leafless, resemble antlers.

Poison sumac, a plant that's dangerous to some people because of the skin irritant it contains, is usually associated with swampy areas. It has white rather than red drupes, and its leaflets have a smooth rather than a serrated edge.

The fuzz or hair on the drupes contains malic acid and, according to some natural-food books, can be used to make a drink resembling lemonade.

Staghorn Sumacs
Paper Birch

Paper Birch

Paper Birch (*Betula papyrifera*) is a common deciduous tree in the coniferous forests of the northern Great Lakes region (**MB** 649). The white bark and golden autumn leaves give paper birches a conspicuous beauty in contrast with evergreens. Further south in Minnesota and Wisconsin, the paper birch, yellow birch, and quaking aspen are more numerous than the conifers.

The leaves of the paper birch are ovate and double-toothed. The bark, when mature, is white with prominent horizontal lenticels (**MB** Fig. 24–14). It peels off the trunk in curled, papery sheets, and was used by Indians to make birchbark canoes. Paper birches are monoecious, having both male and female catkins on a single tree. The seeds are released in samaras (**MB** 338, Table 27–1) in great numbers and may germinate that same season. Birch trees are among the first to establish new growth in areas destroyed by fire. The birch groves are later replaced by fir and spruce (**MB** 679), the climax species in northern regions.

BIRDS

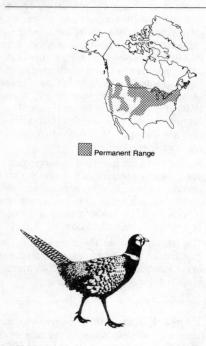

Permanent Range

Ring-Necked Pheasant (*Phasianus cholchicus torquatus*) is the state bird of South Dakota. Originally from Asia, it is one of the few imported species that have proven beneficial rather than harmful.

The blue and red colors of the head, and the white neck and long tail identify the males. The plain brown color of the females serves as a protection from predators during nesting (**MB** 486).

Although successfully established as breeding populations in northern states, ring-necked pheasants have not fared well in the south. Many are raised in pens and released on private hunting lands (**MB** 704). They may run through fields well ahead of hunters or crouch and wait to take off in a startling flurry of flapping wings and loud cackles.

Pheasants feed on grains such as wheat, barley, and corn and on wild seed, berries, and insects. They are so tolerant of human activities that they are often seen flying across highways close to major cities.

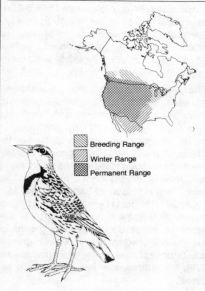

Breeding Range
Winter Range
Permanent Range

Western Meadowlark (*Sturnella neglecta*) is the state bird of North Dakota, where it nests in grass or weeds. This species cannot be visually distinguished from the eastern meadowlark (*Sturnella magna*). Both have a black V on a yellow breast and white outer tail feathers. The songs of the two species, however, are very different, the song of the western meadowlark being more melodious. This difference in song was probably of importance in determining the species (**MB** 167). Since the western species has extended eastward as the forests have been cleared, the two species may overlap in territory, but they do not interbreed (**MB** 172). Both species have a similar diet. In summer they feed mostly on insects such as grasshoppers, crickets, beetles, and caterpillars. In winter, when they migrate south, their intake of seeds increases.

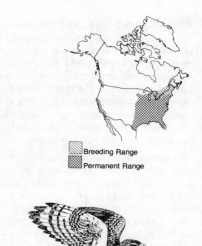

Breeding Range
Permanent Range

Red-Shouldered Hawk (*Buteo lineatus*) and Red-Tailed Hawk (*Buteo jamaicensis*) are often seen soaring high in the sky, even fairly close to cities like Chicago. From great heights their keen eyesight can spot tiny field mice moving in the grassy fields below (**MB** 673). They are valuable in that they keep the rodent population in check and very seldom attack chickens.

As carnivores they are at the top of the food pyramid (**MB** 667). They nest high in trees and search large areas for food. They are often seen perching on fence posts or trees, ready to glide silently down on unsuspecting prey. Their feet are formed to capture and hold prey (**MB** Fig. 37-9), and their sharp beaks are well adapted for tearing flesh (**MB** Fig. 37-6).

The red-tailed hawk is found in all states east of Minnesota and has adapted to a variety of habitats (**MB** 671). It prefers swampy areas in deciduous forests at lower elevations rather than upland forests.

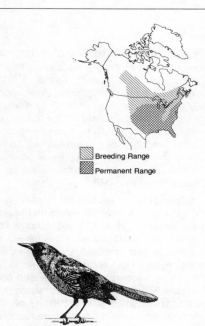

Breeding Range
Permanent Range

Common Grackle (*Quiscalus quiscula*) is a relatively large, blackish bird with contour feathers that show a purple iridescence on the head and a brassy iridescence on the body. The long quill feathers in the tail (**MB** Fig. 37-4) are arranged in a vertical rather than a horizontal plane, giving the tail a rudderlike appearance.

Grackles are gregarious birds, and groups of them may be seen feeding on lawns, in city parks, and in country fields (**MB** 687). Although they are notorious for destroying crops, they also save crops by eating large numbers of insects. Aside from people, their main predators are hawks and owls. Many grackles fall victim to disease spread by parasites, mainly lice (**MB** Fig. 32-12). Grackles are truly omnivorous, and their food varies with the season. They eat grain, insects, fruits, frogs, worms, crayfish, and a host of other organisms. They are aggressive when feeding and are known to raid the nests of other birds and eat their eggs and even young nestlings.

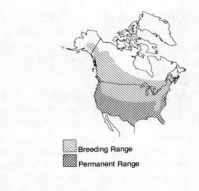

Breeding Range
Permanent Range

Red-Winged Blackbirds (*Agelaius spp.*) are common throughout most of the United States. Two varieties are common in the region. The **Giant Redwing** (*Agelaius phoeniceus arctolegus*) is similar to but larger than the **Eastern Redwing** (*A. p. phoeniceus*) (**MB** 178). The giant variety occupies a more northern territory, and the females have slightly different markings than the eastern variety.

Red-winged blackbirds are among the first arrivals of the spring migration (**MB** 677). About three broods a year insure a busy life of nest building and food gathering. Redwings prefer a diet of insects, and in some cases have saved crops from being destroyed by caterpillars and other larvae. When migrating, however, the large flocks can cause serious damage to grain crops.

Red-winged blackbirds' nests can be found in almost any marshy area. Though many large marshes have been drained or filled in for building sites (**MB** 702), the redwings have adapted, and many now nest in small roadside ditches, close to human activity.

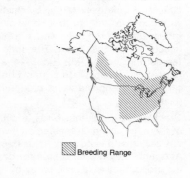

Breeding Range

Black and White Warbler (*Mniotilta varia*) is one of the few warblers in this region that lacks bright colors. **Wood Warblers** are small, flashy, often brightly colored perching birds. Their slender, pointed beaks are adapted for feeding on insects (**MB** Fig. 37–6). Each species of wood warbler has its own feeding habits so that when two or more different species occupy the same area, competition for insects is minimal (**MB** Fig. 50–2).

In spring more than 25 different species of warblers pass through Illinois on their migration north (**MB** 677). Although a few nest in the central states, many have been driven farther north as nesting sites are destroyed. The coniferous forests of northern Michigan, Wisconsin, and Minnesota are favored sites for some (**MB** 650). **Bachman's Warbler** is on the federal government's endangered species list, while **Swainson's Warbler** is listed as threatened.

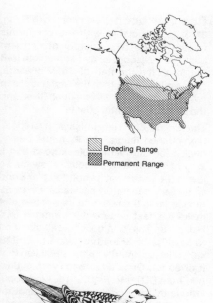

Breeding Range
Permanent Range

Mourning Dove (*Zenaidura macroura*)

(MB 484) is a name derived from the sad, melancholic coo of these grayish tan birds that resemble the extinct passenger pigeons (**MB** 702). Mourning doves make a fluttering noise when they fly and show two white lateral bands on their pointed, triangular tails. They are one of the few birds that nest in every state. They have adapted well to changes in environment and can be seen in city parks, suburban yards, and country fields.

In northern climates they have at least two broods a season. Both parents share in incubating the eggs for about 15 days (**MB** 494). Doves are good examples of altricial birds: their young are hatched extremely helpless (**MB** 496). The parents regurgitate predigested food called pigeon milk into the mouths of the young, which cling to their nest with their delicate feet.

Corn, wheat, and wildflower seeds are doves' main diet. During the fall doves form flocks to migrate south, but a few usually remain behind and depend on bird feeders and seed plants to survive the winter.

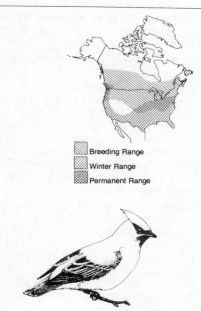

Breeding Range
Winter Range
Permanent Range

Cedar Waxwing (*Bombycilla cedrorum*), is a strikingly beautiful bird. Its pale yellow-brown color and crested head with a black eye mask make it easy to recognize. The name *waxwing* refers to the waxy red tips on some of the secondary wing feathers (**MB** 486).

Cedar waxwings spend most of the year moving from one feeding area to another. Small flocks seem to appear from nowhere, even in the middle of cities like Milwaukee, Wisconsin. They feed frantically on the berries of trees and then are suddenly gone. They are quite tame and, when feeding, will allow people to get close enough to listen to their quiet chirping. Their favorite foods are juniper or cedar berries and wild cherries, including choke cherries. They occasionally eat insects. Waxwings can damage orchards, especially cherry and apple orchards, by eating the flowers or ripened fruit.

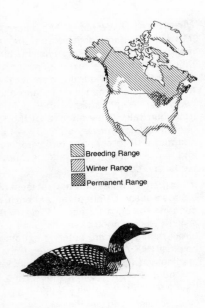

Breeding Range
Winter Range
Permanent Range

Common Loon (*Gavia immer*) (**MB** Fig. 37-3) is associated with the coniferous forests of the lake country of northern Michigan, Wisconsin, and Minnesota (**MB** Fig. 52-8). It is the state bird of Minnesota. Loons migrate south in the winter and can be seen along the Mississippi River and the Gulf and Atlantic coasts.

The loon's call resembles a hysterical, high-pitched laugh. The loon is a heavy, duck-sized bird with a black head and a long neck with a white collar. It swims so low in the water that its spotted black and white back can hardly be seen. Its legs, attached far in the rear, and its webbed feet make it a fast underwater swimmer (**MB** Fig. 37-9). The loon uses its tail-gland oil to keep its body feathers watertight (**MB** 487). It lives primarily on the small fish that it dives for. Once threatened with extinction from DDT (**MB** Fig. 52-15), loon populations in some areas now face another threat. Their shoreline nests are swamped by waves from passing motorboats.

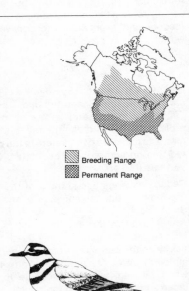

Breeding Range
Permanent Range

Killdeer (*Charadrius vociferus*) has a high-pitched cry that sounds just like its name. Early spring arrivals, killdeers are easily recognized by their long legs and the double black bands across a white breast.

Killdeers are shoreline birds. Their three-toed tracks can be seen along the mud banks of ponds and streams (**MB** Fig. 37-9). Killdeers also frequent fields and lawns, searching for insects. Their nests are nothing more than a slight depression in the ground with a few sticks and pebbles strewn about. It is not unusual for killdeers to nest in the middle of a lawn. Their eggs blend in well with the surroundings and are difficult to see.

Killdeers are precocial birds (**MB** 496). When the eggs hatch, the chicks are a fluffy mass of down feathers (**MB** 486) and are able to run around and feed almost immediately. In protecting the nest, the killdeer instinctively feigns injury to attract attention (**MB** 496). The chicks also display innate behavior by holding still when threatened (**MB** 429).

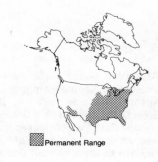

Permanent Range

Cardinal (*Richmondena cardinalis cardinalis*) (**MB** Fig. 33–3) is the state bird of Illinois, where it is a year-round resident. The males are bright red; the females are olive green with tinges of red. Both have crested head feathers, and both sing marvelously well. Their large, strong red beaks are ideal for cracking seeds too large or hard for smaller birds (**MB** Fig. 37–6). Seeds and fruits are their usual diet, but they also eat insects and seem to prefer insects for feeding their young.

In spring the males can sometimes be seen feeding the females as part of a courtship ritual. Cardinals raise about three broods a year and usually nest in heavy thickets. They have been extremely successful in adapting to civilization (**MB** 18). Before 1890 they were found largely south of the Ohio River. Since then they have expanded their range into the northern states and Canada. Their population is still growing, and their range now includes North and South Dakota. Many cardinals depend on backyard feeders to survive the winter months.

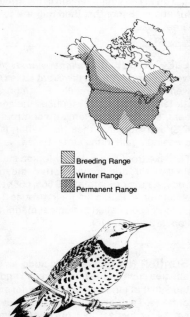

Breeding Range
Winter Range
Permanent Range

Flicker (*Colaptes auratus*) is a large brown woodpecker with a red patch on the back of its head and a black crescent on its breast. The yellow underside of its wings and the white patch on its posterior show when the bird is flying. In the western states the undersides of wings are salmon-colored.

Flickers can be seen in city parks, along tree-lined suburban streets, and in the country. Their beaks are strong and pointed. Flickers can often be heard hammering on trees in their search for insects. Their rapid head movements demand specialized feet for gripping (**MB** 490); the pointed ends of their tail feathers pressed against bark give them added stability.

Flickers are unusual woodpeckers in that they also feed on the ground. They are often seen probing ant nests with their long beaks and sticky tongues (**MB** 488). In winter a few flickers may remain behind to feed on fruits, but most migrate south (**MB** 677).

FISH

Alewives (*Alosa pseudoharengus*) are small, silver, herringlike migrants from the Atlantic that advanced into the upper Great Lakes through Lake Ontario and the Welland Canal, which opened in 1932. The destruction by the lamprey of such predatory fish as the lake trout (**MB** Fig. 34–2) contributed to an alewife population explosion (**MB** 688). Alewives take over spawning beds (**MB** 444) and eat the eggs and young of more economically desirable species.

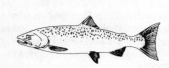

Coho Salmon (*Oncorhynchus kisutch*) is a champion sport fish of the Great Lakes. When hooked, this silver fish often makes wild aerial leaps before being netted. The coho averages five to ten pounds in weight, spawns in rivers and streams (**MB** 444). The coho reaches full growth in three or four years, then spawns and dies. The young remain in the streams for about 18 months, then migrate to the Great Lakes.

Lake Trout (*Salvelinus namaycush*) were once plentiful in the Great Lakes and were fished commercially. Pollution and the lamprey drastically reduced their numbers, but now, with lamprey control (**MB** 433) and stocking, their population is increasing again in the Great Lakes.

The lake trout has a deeply forked caudal fin (**MB** 437) and lightly spotted, greenish body. As top predators (**MB** 665, 666), they accumulate PCB's in their tissues in a phenomenon called biological magnification (**MB** Fig. 52–15).

Sunfish (*Leponis spp.*) include several species such as the pumpkinseed and the bluegill that inhabit ponds and quiet areas of lakes. Their average length is about 20 cm (eight inches), but in over-populated ponds they may be much smaller (**MB** 685).

They are disc-shaped, with large eyes that can move independently of one another (**MB** Fig. 34–13).

Walleyed Pike (*Stizostedion vitreum*) is
the state fish of Minnesota. It is stocked in many lakes and is an aggressive predator (**MB** 686), sometimes replacing bass and lake trout. Walleyes average between one and four pounds in weight and live from 10 to 12 years. They are olive or yellow-brown with light-colored eyes and sharp teeth. They spawn in lakes and streams. The newly hatched fry are attached to yolk sacs (**MB** 444). Within a few days they start feeding on zooplankton, especially *Daphnia* (**MB** Fig. 31–6), then later feed on other fish. Schools of walleyes often feed at night, close to shore.

Carp (*Cyprinnus carpio*) are recognized
by their large scales and by two paired barbels over a toothless suckerlike mouth. One record carp caught in Clearwater, Minnesota, weighed 55.5 pounds (25 kg).

Carp are selectively bred (**MB** 151) for food in many countries but not in the U.S. Introduced from Europe, carp are detrimental to some lakes where they root out bottom plants, muddy the waters, and replace other species. They can, however, live in polluted waters (**MB** 706) unsuitable for other fish. All the varieties of goldfish belong to the carp family.

Smallmouth Bass (*Micropterus dolomieu*) and Largemouth Bass (*M. salmoides*)
are both native American fish. They may live in the same lake, but they occupy different habitats (**MB** 671). The smallmouth prefers deeper, cooler waters, while the largemouth is found in warm shallows.

In a side view, the mouth of the smallmouth does not extend farther back than the eye. Females lay between 2,000 and 20,000 eggs (**MB** 444) in nests prepared and guarded by the males. Both the smallmouth and largemouth bass are aggressive carnivores (**MB** 437) and sometimes devour their own young.

Rainbow Trout (*Salmo gairdneri*) is one of the most popular game fish in the world. Through selective breeding (**MB** 152) varieties have been developed for different environments such as lakes or streams. Unlike the brook trout, the rainbow trout is not a native species but has been imported into this region. Rainbow trout show countershading (**MB** 436). They have a dark dorsal and a light ventral surface and a pink band along their lateral line (**MB** Fig. 34–8). The rainbow trout in the Great Lakes are called steelheads. They have developed into a silvery fish with a steel-blue colored head and back.

Smelt (*Osmerus mordax*) are landlocked fish originally from the Atlantic Ocean. They were introduced into a small Michigan lake in 1906 to serve as food for the salmon that were also being stocked in the lake. Now they are found in many northern lakes, including the Great Lakes. Obeying their instincts (**MB** 444), they migrate up streams to spawn each spring, and at that time many are netted by sport fishermen. Some are also netted commercially. Smelt eat invertebrates, including crustaceans and insects, and in turn are eaten by larger fish such as bass and salmon (**MB** Fig. 49–3).

Lake Sturgeon (*Acipenser fulvenscens*), a primitive fish with a cartilaginous skeleton (**MB** 434) and bony plates rather than scales. Its fossil ancestors can be dated back to the Devonian period (**MB** Fig. 13–7). Some sturgeons reach over two meters in length and weigh over 136 kg (300 pounds). Four tactile barbels (**MB** 442) dangle in front of a sucking mouth and detect invertebrates, plants, and small fish in muddy lake bottoms. Sturgeon are listed as threatened in Illinois and Michigan and as an endangered species in Ohio and North Dakota (**MB** 701). Alien species of sturgeon are being transplanted in some areas of the country in an effort to harvest caviar.

AMPHIBIANS AND REPTILES

Eastern Tiger Salamander (*Ambystoma tigrinum*) (**MB** Fig. 35–3) is found in many areas of the U.S. It is a nocturnal carnivore and feeds on worms, sowbugs, insects, and almost any other animal it can overpower. Tiger salamanders prefer permanent ponds, but they can be found under logs, in drainage pipes or tiles, or in other places that are wet and dark. The tiger salamander has no teeth and is harmless to humans. The females lay about 1,000 eggs in small masses of about 50 eggs attached to some vegetation under water.

Spring Peeper (*Hyla crucifer*) is a small frog less than 2.5 cm long, with a dark X on its back and a dark band between its eyes. In spring the high-pitched calls of spring peepers are heard from almost every marshy area in yards, fields, or woods. When approached, spring peepers suddenly become quiet. Occasionally a spring peeper may be seen with its white throat expanded sending air through its larynx (**MB** 456). Eggs are laid and tadpoles hatched in about 12 days (**MB** Fig. 35–12). Those few that reach maturity hibernate through the winter (**MB** 462). Peepers are usually seen only in the breeding season.

Common Toad (*Bufo americanus*) (**MB** Fig. 35–4) returns to ponds and marshes to breed at three or four years of age. A single female may lay 4,000 to 10,000 eggs in long strands. Often the tadpoles are so numerous under water that they appear like dark clouds. Many are eaten by pond carnivores and later, on land, by birds and snakes. Large parotoid glands behind toads' eyes secrete a milky, distasteful poison (**MB** 452). Many toads "play dead" when hurt or roughly treated. Otherwise they have few defenses except protective coloration.

Box Turtle

Box Turtle (*Terrapene spp.*) is a land turtle found in grassy woodlands, meadows, and thickets. Its outstanding feature is its hinged plastron (**MB 474**) which can close tightly against the upper shell, enclosing its head, feet, and tail to protect the animal from danger. The box turtle feeds on fruits, leafy greens, insects, and grubs. The eastern box turtle (**MB** Fig. 36–9) is classified as a threatened species in Michigan. **Blanding's Turtle,** a semi-box turtle that only partially closes, is a protected species in Minnesota and a threatened species in Wisconsin. Box turtles are especially fond of strawberries and blackberries.

Common Snapping Turtle (*Chelydra serpentina*) averages 20 pounds or more in weight (**MB** Fig. 36–9). It prefers permanent streams and ponds where it feeds on fish, crayfish, and anything else it can catch, including adult waterfowl. The snapping turtle has a long tail with horny shields and a large head that extends far from its algae-covered carapace. Its plastron is cross-shaped (**MB** 474). After mating, a female snapping turtle lays about 20 eggs in a sandy nest close to water (**MB** 468). The snapper is dangerous. It can move quite rapidly and amputate a finger with one bite.

Garter Snake (*Thamnophis spp.*)(**MB** Fig. 36–12) is familiar, abundant, and widely distributed. Most have three longitudinal stripes, sometimes red, orange, or yellow, that help identify the species. Garter snakes can be found in wooded city parks, in leafy waste under suburban hedges, or in country swamps. They feed primarily on frogs, toads, worms, and insects. When handled, they can nip or may secrete a foul-smelling fluid from glands close to their tails. Garter snakes are ovoviviparous (**MB** 479), each female producing about 25 young a season. Large numbers hibernate together in rocky crevices and caves.

ECOSYSTEMS

Mixed-Grass Prairie (**MB** 652)

1. big bluestem grass (p 8)
2. switch grass (p 8)
3. thirteen-lined ground squirrel
4. badger
5. coyote
6. prairie chicken
7. meadow vole
8. grasshopper (MB 401)
9. harvest mouse
10. long-tailed weasel

11. black-footed ferret
12. cone flower
13. blue grama grass (p 8)
14. needle grass (p 8)
15. cottonwood (p 9)
16. bison (MB 505)
17. meadowlark (p 16)
18. red-winged blackbird (p 18)
19. prairie rattlesnake
20. sharp-tailed grouse

21. bobolink
22. grasshopper sparrow
23. upland plover
24. wolfberry
25. lark bunting
26. black-tailed prairie dog
27. pocket gopher
28. silverberry
29. great horned owl
30. locoweed

31. droop-seed grass
32. pronghorn
33. jack rabbit
34. swift (kit) fox
35. kangaroo rat
36. prairie phlox
37. sunflower (MB 338)
38. prairie rose
39. prairie deer mouse
40. sough grass (p 8)

Coniferous Forest (**MB** 649)

1. rock tripe lichen
2. quaking aspen
3. black bear
4. beaver (MB 499, 504)
5. blueberry
6. paper birch (p 15)
7. swallowtail butterfly (MB 409)
8. brachen ferns
9. horsetails (MB 275)
10. fleur-de-lis
11. Jack pine
12. white pine (p 11)
13. black spruce
14. porcupine
15. balsam fir
16. yellow water-lily
17. moose (MB 172, 178)
18. wolf
19. ruffed grouse (p 23)
20. lynx
21. loon (p 20)
22. herring gull
23. white-tailed deer (MB 18)
24. osprey
25. great horned owl
26. marsh marigold
27. red-breasted nuthatch
28. northern pike
29. leech
30. red-backed vole
31. walleyed pike (23)
32. snowshoe hare
33. chickadee
34. muskrat
35. lily of the valley
36. juniper (MB 277)
37. kingfisher (MB 484)
38. snowy owl
39. pussy willow (p 14)
40. eastern garter snake (MB 479)

Deciduous Forest (**MB 651**)

1. white oak (p 9)
2. sugar maple (p 12)
3. bur oak (p 11)
4. shagbark hickory (p 14)
5. white trillium (p 5)
6. white ash
7. wild black cherry
8. basswood
9. redstart
10. wood thrush
11. black walnut
12. white-tailed deer (MB 18)
13. marbled salamander
14. hawthorn (p 13)
15. dog's-tooth violet (p 5)
16. millipede (MB 387, 397)
17. hackberry
18. bigtooth aspen
19. box turtle (p 26)
20. black rat snake
21. opossum (MB 508)
22. grey squirrel
23. downy woodpecker
24. beech
25. northern red oak
26. white-footed mouse
27. eastern mole
28. eastern chipmunk
29. yellow birch
30. American elm (p 10)
31. butternut hickory
32. grey fox
33. tree frog (MB 454)
34. raccoon (MB 514)
35. bracket fungus (MB 247)
36. Ohio buckeye
37. maidenhair fern
38. white-breasted nuthatch
39. Jack-in-the-pulpit
40. hemlock

Shrubby Weedy Field

1. lamb's quarters
2. burdock (p 3)
3. Queen Anne's lace (p 5)
4. American toad (p 25)
5. red fox
6. hawthorn (p 13)
7. groundhog
8. field bindweed (p 4)
9. eastern cottontail
10. black-eyed Susan (p 7)

11. buckthorn
12. jewelweed
13. daisy fleabane
14. deer mouse
15. common milkweed (p 7)
16. pocket gopher
17. garter snake (MB 479)
18. monarch butterfly
19. staghorn sumac (p 15)
20. striped skunk

21. ring-necked pheasant (p 16)
22. least weasel
23. St.-John's-wort
24. mullein
25. goldenrod (p 3)
26. ragweed
27. thirteen-lined ground squirrel
28. red-tailed hawk
29. meadow vole
30. yellow-shafted flicker

31. kingbird
32. barn swallow
33. young cottonwood (p 9)
34. meadowlark
35. robin (MB 484)
36. mourning dove (p 19)
37. common flicker (p 21)
38. blue jay
39. white sweet clover (p 7)
40. dandelion (p 6)

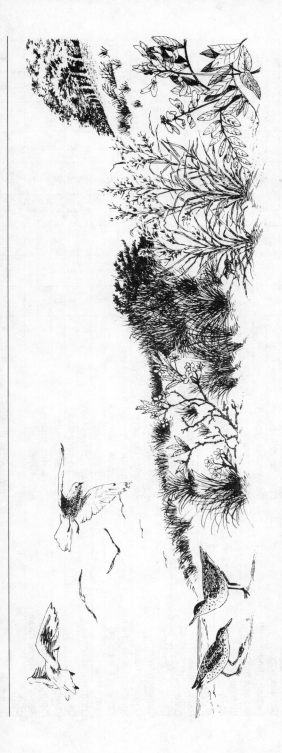

Lake Shoreline-Sand Dune Succession

1. marran grass
2. little bluestem
3. sand cherry
4. choke cherry
5. creeping juniper
6. cottonwood (p 9)
7. willow (p 14)
8. ring-billed gull (MB 640)
9. herring gull
10. spotted sandpiper

11. tiger beetle
12. horsefly
13. digger wasp
14. toad (p 25)
15. burrowing spider
16. robber fly
17. termite (MB 408)
18. kingbird
19. bluebell
20. long-horned locust

21. field cricket
22. camel cricket
23. raccoon (MB 514)
24. Jack pine
25. white pine (p 11)
26. black oak
27. white oak (p 9)
28. elm (p 10)
29. basswood
30. maple (p 12, MB 294)

31. beech
32. velvet ant
33. fern (MB 274)
34. poison ivy (p 8)
35. opossum (MB 508)
36. skunk
37. deer mouse
38. cabbage butterfly
39. chickadee
40. six-lined lizard

SOME ENDANGERED AND THREATENED SPECIES

	Federal List	Ohio	Indiana	Illinois	Michigan	Wisconsin	Minnesota	N. Dakota	S. Dakota
Mammals									
Badger — *Taxidea taxus*			E						E
Black-footed ferret — *Mustela nigripes*	E							E	E
Bobcat — *Lynx rufus*		E	E	T					
Canada lynx — *Lynx canadensis*									
Eastern timber wolf — *Canis lupus lycaon*	E		E	E	E	E	T		
Indiana bat — *Myotis sodalis*	E	E	E	E	E	E		E	
Pine martin — *Martes americana*					T	E			
River otter — *Lutra canadensis*			E					E	T
Birds									
Bald eagle — *Haliaeatus leucocephalus*	E	E		E	E	E	E	E	T
Barn owl — *Tyto alba*				E	T	E			
Bachman's warbler — *Vermivora bachmanii*	E								
Common tern — *Sterna hirundo*		E		E	T	E			
Cooper's hawk — *Accipiter cooperii*				E	T	T			
Greater prairie chicken — *Tympanuchus cupido pinnatus*				E	T	T		T	T
Kirtland's warbler — *Dendroica kirtlandii*	E	E		E	E				
Least tern — *Sterna albifrons*				E				T	E
Loggerhead shrike — *Lanius ludovicianus*				T	T	T		T	
Osprey — *Pandion haliaetus*		E		E	T	E	E	E	T
Peregrine falcon — *Falco peregrinus*	E	E		E	T	E		E	
Piping plover — *Charadrius melodus*				E	T	E		E	
Red-shouldered hawk — *Buteo lineatus*				E	T	T			
Fish									
Blue pike — *Stizostedion vitreum glaucum*	E	E							